Stage 2

Pop Festival

**Longman
Structural
Readers**

Ian Serraillier

Illustrated by
Douglas Hall

This is Paul Dupont. He's a French boy, and he has come to England. He's staying with the Davieses. They have a daughter, Catherine. Catherine has stayed at his home in France. The two families are friends.

Paul likes music, and he plays the guitar.

"Sing a French song, Paul," Catherine said.

"All right, my little cabbage," Paul said.

"Cabbage! That's not my name!"

"It's a good name in France."

"But I don't like cabbage. Please don't say that here."

"All right, Cat."

"What's that, Paul? Is my daughter a cat?" Mr Davies said. "Are you saying that?"

"I can't easily say 'Catherine'. But I can say 'Cat' very easily."

"Ugh! I don't like cats," Mr Davies said. "Do you, Paul?"

"I like Cat," Paul said.

"And I like Kate," Catherine said. Paul held her hand.

"Oh," Mr Davies said.

Catherine – Cat – Kate – laughed. Then she put the guitar into his hands. "Take this, Paul," she said, "and please sing a French song."

Paul sang one. He sang two – three – four – five songs. They loved them.

"One day you'll be a pop star, Paul," Catherine said.

"A pop star! Me?"

"Yes, wearing Dad's hat." She went and found it. "Ugh, that thing!" Mr Davies said.

"Put it on, Paul. Oh, that's wonderful!"

3

On Monday Mr Davies drove his wife and Paul and Catherine to the sea. They drove to the beach and left the car on the road. For some time Mr Davies played cricket with Paul and Catherine. Then he sat down on the beach.

"It's very hot," Mr Davies said. He put a newspaper over his head and went to sleep.

Paul and Catherine swam in the sea.

Suddenly a boy's head came up between them. "Hello, Catherine!" the boy said. And he laughed.

"Oh, it's George!" Catherine said. She knew George. He was a friend of the family, and he went to her school.

"George, this is Paul, my French friend," she said.

"Hello, Paul," George said.

"Hello, George."

George liked Catherine very much.

("We've been friends for a long time," he thought. "But Paul's here now. Will she like me now?")

He said, "You write long letters to him, Catherine. I know. He's your — "

"Come and eat!" Mrs Davies called from the beach.

"Mum's calling. We must go," Catherine said quickly. "Goodbye."

"Yes. Go back to the beach. And you can go back to France, Paul," George shouted. He dived and pulled Paul under the water.

George held Paul under the water for a long time.

"Paul!" Catherine cried.

"Come and eat, you two," Mrs Davies called.

Paul's head came up. His face was white.

"Oh, Paul! Are you all right?" said Catherine.

"Ha, ha! French frog!" George laughed.

"Ha, ha! English pig!" Paul cried. And he dived and pulled George under the water. He held him there. Then he swam to the beach with Catherine.

"French frog!" George shouted.

"English pig!" Paul shouted back. He laughed, but Catherine was worried.

"Here's a sandwich for you, Catherine," Mrs Davies said.

"Here's a sandwich for your Dad – oh, he's asleep. I'll put it on his plate. I've put some French mustard in these sandwiches for you, Paul. You're cold, my dear. Here they are. The mustard will warm you."

The French mustard and some hot coffee quickly warmed Paul. The colour came back to his face.

"Look, Paul," Catherine said. She took the newspaper off her father's head. "Pop Festival," she read. "Pop Festival on the Island. Four days of music. The Loving Cups – the Why –

the Misfits – José and his guitar. It'll be good. Shall we go, Paul?"

"Oh, yes!"

"Dad!"

But Dad was asleep. A seagull flew down and flew off with his sandwich.

7

Mr Davies moved. His eyes opened. "Oh, my nose is burning! Where's my newspaper?"

"Here," Catherine said. "Look, Dad. A Pop Festival on — "

"Where's my sandwich?"
Catherine laughed. "A seagull — "

"Why are you laughing?"

"Eat this, Mr Davies," Paul said.

"It's one of his sandwiches, Dad. Take it."

"Very kind," Mr Davies said. He put a big piece in his mouth. .

"Ouch! My tongue's burning! What is it?"

"French mustard," Mrs Davies said. "I put it in for Paul."

"Oh, my tongue! And my nose! Fire!"

"Wait a minute," Paul said. He ran off – and quickly ran back. "Here's an ice cream, Mr Davies. Put it on your tongue."

"On your nose, too," Catherine said. She put some ice cream on his nose. "We're going to the Pop Festival on Friday, Dad."

"Oh – are you? Well – come back on Saturday. Now put the French mustard in the sea. It'll warm the water. I'm going to swim."

It was Friday – the first day of the Pop Festival.

"Here are two sleeping-bags," Mrs Davies said. "Take them with you. Here's some food too."

"Don't forget your guitar, Paul," Catherine said.

"No, I won't. Er – can I take your

hat, please, Mr Davies?" Paul asked. "It's a very good hat for a pop festival."

"*That* hat?" Mr Davies laughed. "Yes. Take it. I don't want it. Shall we go now?"

They said goodbye to Mrs Davies and got into the car.

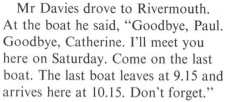

Mr Davies drove to Rivermouth. At the boat he said, "Goodbye, Paul. Goodbye, Catherine. I'll meet you here on Saturday. Come on the last boat. The last boat leaves at 9.15 and arrives here at 10.15. Don't forget."

"We won't forget," Catherine said.

The boat went out into the open sea. It was full of young people.

"Look, Cat – er, Kate. Is that George over there?" Paul asked.

"Where? I can't see."

"Under the — Oh, he's gone now."

"Good."

The boat arrived at the island, and the young people left it.

The roads were full. The buses were full. Catherine and Paul walked to the Pop Festival.

It was a very long walk.

The Pop Festival was on a hill. There were some big tents, an open stage with loudspeakers, a farmhouse with white walls, and a windmill. There were fields and trees on every side.

"Hello, you people from the boat," the loudspeakers said.

"Four days of music. Pay your money and come into the field."

"This festival is for Peace!" a voice cried. "Peace doesn't have fences. Take the fence down!"

"Don't touch the fence," a man shouted.

Some people didn't want to pay their money. They went over the fence. One boy tore his trousers on it.

"He's torn his trousers," Paul said. "We'll buy tickets – not new trousers, Kate."

They bought tickets and went in.

Catherine and Paul sat down on the grass. They listened to the music from the loudspeakers. But they didn't stay there.

"People! Hundreds of people! You sit down, and they stand on you. We must move on, Paul."

They moved on. And they listened to the voices: "Where's Maureen?" – "Where's Bob?" – "Where's Fred?" – "Have you seen Brenda? I can't find her." – "Have you seen my boy friend? He has long green hair."

"I don't want to lose you, Paul," Catherine said.

"You won't."

"You can easily lose people here. Perhaps I'll lose you in the morning. What will I do then?"

"Meet me at the boat," Paul said. "But you won't lose me."

"Perhaps I won't, but I wanted to know."

He took her hand and they walked up the hill.

"Oh, Paul! Where's the guitar?"

"You had it on the grass, Kate."

"I gave it to you."

"I gave it to you. I remember."

"No, you didn't. I — "

"Is this it?" a voice asked.

It was George – in a red shirt and a long yellow coat. "You left it on the grass, Catherine."

"Oh, thank you, George."

"I'll give it to your pop star."

("Pop star – not French frog?" Paul thought. "Is he laughing at me?")

Paul looked at George's clothes. "Thank you, Gentleman George."

("Gentleman – not English pig?" George thought. "Is he laughing at me?")

"My guitar will thank you too," Paul said. And he sang a French song for George.

People in the field listened, then they clapped.

"That guy with the guitar – he's good," a man said. "Ask him to sing again."

"Please, Paul," Catherine said.

Paul sang again. The people clapped.

"What's the guy's name?" the man asked.

"Paul Dupont," Catherine said.

"I won't forget it. One day he'll be a pop star."

"Who's that man, George?" Catherine asked.

"Mike Barker. He's the organiser."

"The organiser of the festival? Oh, isn't that wonderful?" Catherine clapped her hands. Then she looked at George's face. "What is it, George? Are you angry? Don't be angry. Paul's my friend. And you are too."

Without a word, George left them.

Paul and Catherine walked up the field and sat down in a good place. They listened and ate their food. The sun went down, and they got out their sleeping-bags. The people near them had sleeping-bags, and some had tents.

"Hello, people of the night," said a voice on the loudspeakers.

"That's Mike Barker's voice," Catherine said.

"Light your matches. Make stars on the hill," Mike said. "Blow out the stars – one – two – three – *now*! Good night!"

"GOOD NIGHT!"

"Paul, did you see that yellow tent?" Catherine asked. "It's George's tent. In the light of the matches I saw his face."

"Don't worry, Kate, I'll look after you. You'll be all right."

A cold wind blew in from the sea.
"You aren't asleep, Kate."
"No."
"Do you like George?"
"Yes – No – Oh, I don't know.
He *was* my friend."
"I know. – Don't worry, Kate.
Go to sleep."

The night was very cold. But they
were warm in their sleeping-bags and
went to sleep.

"Good morning!" Mike said on the
loudspeakers. "The sun's up. Get up.
Eat your breakfast. The music's at
10 o'clock."

Catherine and Paul made some
coffee.
"George is asleep," Catherine
said. "We'll pack up our things
and move."
They packed up their things and
moved near to the stage.

The music was very good. Mike Barker was on the stage. He had a microphone, and he introduced the music. They heard the Loving Cups and the Why and the Misfits. They sat and listened happily for hours.

"When will he introduce José?" Paul asked.

"José's not here yet. I asked. – Oh, look! Here's Mike Barker."

"Hey, you – the guy with the guitar!" Mike said. "José can't come. I've had a telegram. Will you play for us, Paul?"

"What, me?"

"Yes."

"On the stage?"

"Why not?"

"But I'm not José. People won't like it."

"They love French songs. And you're good with that guitar."

"Please, Paul," Catherine said.

Paul stood up. Mike took his hand and pulled him on to the stage.

"We – want – José!" the people shouted.

"Well, you can't have him. He can't come," Mike said. And he held up the telegram.

"Here's Paul," Mike said. "French Paul from Paris. He's great! – Go on, boy! Those French songs."

"French frog-noises!" Catherine heard. It was George, just behind her. She went quickly to the side of the stage.

Paul sang. The people clapped. He sang a second song, and they clapped and clapped.

He looked at the sea of happy faces. He wanted to see Catherine. ("Is *she* happy?" he thought. "Where is she?")

He looked again, and saw – George!

George shouted angrily, "We want to hear José – not this French frog!"

"Yes!" the boy with torn trousers shouted. "We bought our tickets for José!"

A third boy shouted, "Pull this French frog off the stage!"

Some people shouted, "Be quiet!"

"All right," George shouted to Paul. "Play José's song."

"What's the name of the song?" Paul asked.

"*Say it Again*!"

"What's the name of the song?"

"*SAY IT AGAIN*!"

"But I've said it again. Can't you hear?"

"No – Yes – Oh, you – "

The people laughed – not at Paul, but at George. They clapped again for Paul.

George was very angry. "I'll get you, you French frog!" he shouted.

"Don't listen to him. Sing again!" people shouted. But Paul didn't hear. He was worried. "Where is Kate?" he thought. "I said, 'I'll look after you, Kate.' But I can't look after her now – I'm up here. And George is down there. And I can't see her. I must find her. I must."

He put his guitar down on the stage and jumped to the ground.

"Get him!" George shouted.

"No!" the people cried. "Leave him! Don't touch him!"

"Get him!" Mr Torn Trousers and Mr Festival-for-Peace shouted.

"Stop that!" cried Mike Barker.

Catherine saw Paul's guitar on the stage, and she picked it up.

"Hey! That's not your guitar."

"But you know me, Mike. I'm — "

"Paul's friend. Sorry, love. It's this noise. – BE QUIET! – Don't be frightened, love."

"Can you see Paul?"

"What, here? We've got half the people of England in this field. BE QUIET! WAIT A MINUTE! — Don't worry, love. Paul's got long legs. He'll come back. Take the guitar. And take this money for him – for your pop star."

Paul saw George and his friends. He ran. The three boys shouted, and they ran too. Paul ran past the farmhouse, and came to the windmill.

The door of the windmill was open. He ran in and shut it – BANG! – in their faces. He ran up the ladder to the first floor and shut the

trap-door. Paul heard the boys at the door and on the ladder. He ran up the ladder to the second floor. He pulled a heavy bag on top of the second trap-door.

"Push!" George said. "Push!" The heavy bag moved.

Paul looked out of the window. He saw the fields and the sea, and one sail of the windmill. The sail didn't move. – But the trap-door moved. He saw George's head.

"We've got him!" George shouted.

Paul jumped out of the window on to the sail. He saw George's angry red face at the window. He looked down – and saw a dark pond. He walked slowly to the end of the sail. And he jumped – not into the pond. He ran to the windmill door.

"Now they can't get out," Paul thought. "And I can go back to Catherine."

"Hey, you!" It was the farmer, and he had a pitchfork in his hand. "What's this? What's this?" "A pitchfork."

"No, no, no!" the farmer said. "What are you doing here?"

"Very well, thank you."

"Don't be stupid, boy. Come here."

"Where?"

"Here. No, not there. Here! Don't be stupid!"

"I'm not stupid," Paul said. "I'm French. I don't understand your English."

"Do you understand this?" The farmer pointed to his pitchfork.

"Yes." Paul wanted to run – but he said, "Look!" He pointed to the window of the windmill.

The farmer looked up at the window, and he saw George's frightened face. He looked down angrily at Paul. – But Paul wasn't there.

"Where's the boy gone? He's run into my barn. I'll catch him."

He pointed his pitchfork and ran to the barn.

There were two dustbins near the barn door. The farmer ran past the dustbins. He looked in the barn, and then he came out again.

Quietly the lid of a dustbin moved. Two eyes showed – then a nose – then a face. It was Paul.

The dustbin had a bad smell, and Paul wanted to get out.

Suddenly he saw the farmer. The dustbin lid went down. CLANG!

"What's that noise?" the farmer cried. "The dustbins?" He went to the dustbins.

CRACK! CRASH!

"What's that?" The farmer ran back to the windmill. It was the bottom window. There was a boy in it – George. A piece of the window fell out. George saw the farmer, and he wanted to get out of the window quickly. But he didn't look under the window.

SPLASH! He fell into the pond.
SQUAWK! The ducks flew away. His
head went under. He stood up, fell
down again, got out.
His clothes and face were black.
Only his eyes were white.

"Got you!" the farmer said, and
he held George's ear.

He called to two of his men, "Open
the door and look in the windmill."
They went in and pulled George's
two friends out.

The farmer looked angrily at the
three boys. "Get out!" he said. "Don't
come near here again, or I'll pitchfork
you into my pond.

Get out!"

George was angry too – and
frightened. He opened his mouth
to speak. The pitchfork moved in the
sunlight. He shut his mouth and ran.
His friends ran too, over the fields and
hills.

Quietly Paul got out of the dustbin.

"I can go back now," he thought. "I must go and find Catherine. Poor Kate! Is she all right?"

He ran to the field. "I must find her," he thought. "But where?

Look at the people! Hundreds – thousands of them! Some are going, and some are arriving. Some are standing, and some are sitting on the grass. – Grass? – I can't see any grass. I can see paper – paper bags, paper plates,

paper cups, paper this and paper that – "

He looked here and there, but where was Catherine? Perhaps Mike Barker knew. He looked for Mike, but where was he too? Where?

Suddenly Paul looked at his watch. "It's 8.15! The last boat leaves at 9.15. And I said, 'Meet me at the boat.' I must run."

He left the Pop Festival and ran down the road to the town.

"Can I get to the boat by 9.15? Will she be there?"

Yes, Catherine was at the boat. She remembered her father's "Don't forget", and she remembered Paul's words, "Meet me at the boat."

She was there by 8 o'clock. She had the guitar and her things and Paul's things and the money for Paul.

She waited for Paul at the gangway. At 9 o'clock it was dark. There were lights on the boat.

People went up the gangway – hundreds of them – but she didn't see Paul. A bell rang.

"The boat's going now," the man at the gangway cried.

The bell rang again.

"Are you coming, miss?"

"I haven't seen Paul. Perhaps he's already on the boat," Catherine thought. And she ran up the gangway.

The boat moved. She looked sadly at the land.

Suddenly she saw a boy. He ran to the gangway.

"Stand back!" the man cried, and he held him back.

The light was on the boy's face. "Paul!" Catherine cried.

The boat was full.

Catherine was unhappy and very tired. She sat on her bag, shut her eyes, and went to sleep.

Voices – voices – voices. Catherine's eyes opened. She saw the lights of a big ship.

" . . . going to New York," a voice said.

"What's that boat over there?" Catherine heard.

"It's a hovercraft. Going to Rivermouth."

"It's moving very quickly."

"Yes. The hovercraft can get from the island to Rivermouth in ten minutes. I don't like them – noisy."

The boat arrived. "Is Dad here?" Yes, she saw him under the lights.

The people left the boat, and she waited. Then she walked slowly down the gangway.

"Ah, there you are, Catherine," Mr Davies said. "Where's Paul?"

There wasn't any answer.

"Where *is* he?" Mr Davies asked.

"On the island. I've lost him – "

"Lost him?"

"Yes."

"No!"

"Oh, Dad! Don't be angry.
I'm very unhappy. What can we do?"

"Put the guitar in the car, or you'll
lose that too."

She put it in the car.

"Now we must think," Mr Davies
said. "Paul's on the island —"

"No, he isn't. He's here." It was

Paul's voice. Catherine looked. She
saw – the hat. She flew to him.

"Oh, Paul! That's wonderful! Oh
I'm — "

"Did you swim here, Paul?"
Mr Davies said.

"I came on the !ast hovercraft.
But I've lost my guitar."

"It's in the car," Catherine said.

"Oh, Kate!"

"Oh, Paul!"

They got in the car and
Mr Davies drove off.

"Did you like the
Pop Festival?" he asked.

"Oh, yes," Catherine said. And she spoke of Paul.

" . . . and then he sang a second song. The people loved it. They clapped and clapped."

"Yes — " Mr Davies said — "Yes — and then? And what did you do then?"

He didn't get an answer. Paul and Catherine didn't say a word. They just thought.

Paul thought a lot: "The pitch-fork – my poor English – the smelly dustbin – Gentleman George in the pond – and my dear, kind Kate! Oh, I shan't forget that Pop Festival."

But dear, kind Kate thought just one thing: "My pop star – the guy with the guitar!"

Exercises

1. Look at this:
   Paul Dupont: He's a French boy.
   Now finish these:

   1. Catherine Davies: She's ....
   2. Mr Davies: ....
   3. Mrs Davies: ....
   4. Paul's song: It's ....
   5. George: ....

2. Look at pages 5–9.
   Example: Where did George pull Paul? (water)
   Answer: He pulled him *under the water*.

   1. Where did Mrs Davies put Mr Davies's sandwich? (plate)
   2. Where did Mrs Davies put the mustard? (sandwich)
   3. Where did Catherine see the words "Pop Festival"? (newspaper)
   4. Where did Mr Davies put the piece of sandwich? (mouth)
   5. Where did Catherine put the ice cream? (nose)

3. Look at pages 10–12.
   Can you make 10 *good* sentences?

There	was	some big tents	beside	the boat
	were	an open stage	in	the hill
		white walls	on	the stage
		loudspeakers	near	the farmhouse
		hundreds of people		the grass
		a windmill		the field

4. Look at pages 13–18.
   Example: Whose was the long yellow coat?
   Answer: It was George's coat.

   1. Whose was the guitar?
   2. Whose was the voice on the loudspeakers?
   3. Whose was the yellow tent?
   4. Whose was the hat on Paul's head?
   5. "French frog-noises!" – Whose words were those?

5. *Example:*   Page 20, picture 2: Paul — guitar on the stage. It's there now.
   Answer: Paul *has put his* guitar on the stage.

	Page	picture	
1.	20	2	Paul — to the ground. He's there now.
2.	20	3	Catherine — Paul's guitar. It's in her hands.
3.	21	2	Paul — to the windmill. He's there now.
4.	21	3	Paul — on the trap-door. It's there now.
5.	24	1	Paul — into the dustbin. He's there now.

6. These sentences need **two words**. **One** of the words is *must* or *can't*.
   Example: Page 26: Paul — Catherine in the field.
   Answer: Paul *can't see* Catherine in the field.

	Page	
1.	26	He — Mike Barker.
2.	27	He — to the boat.
3.	28	Paul — on the boat.
4.	29	Catherine — the boat at Rivermouth.
5.	30	She — the guitar in the car.

7. Answer *Yes, I did* **or** *No, I didn't*.
   Did you like   Catherine?
                  George?
                  Paul?
                  this story?
                  the dustbin?
                  Mr Festival-for-Peace?
                  Mr Torn Trousers?
                  Mike Barker?
                  the pictures?
                  Mr Davies?